# The big hole

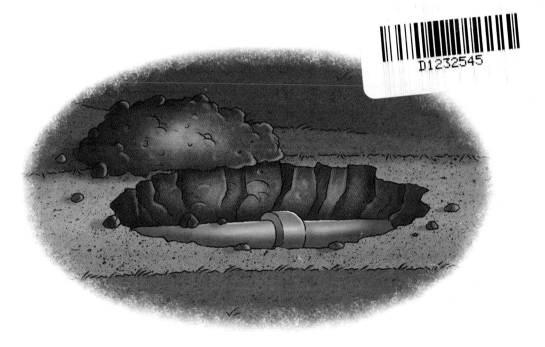

Look at the cars.

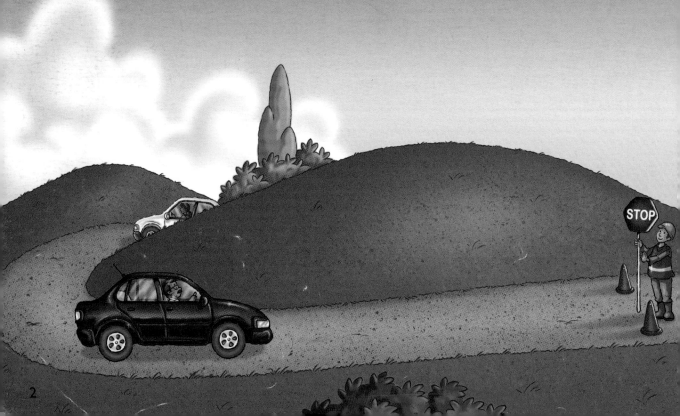

Look at the big hole!

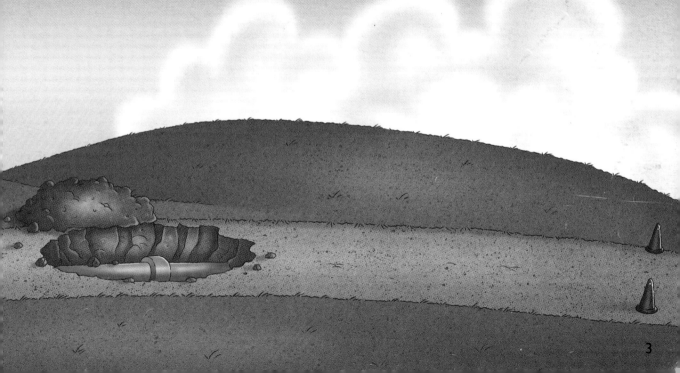

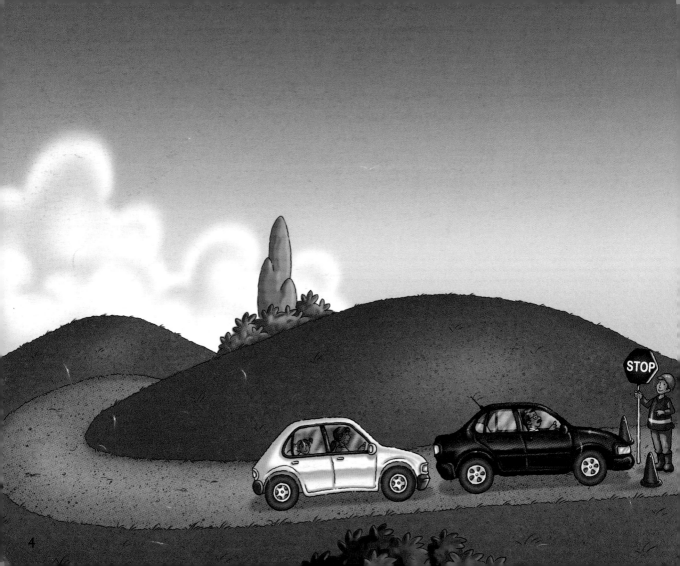

Here is the digger.

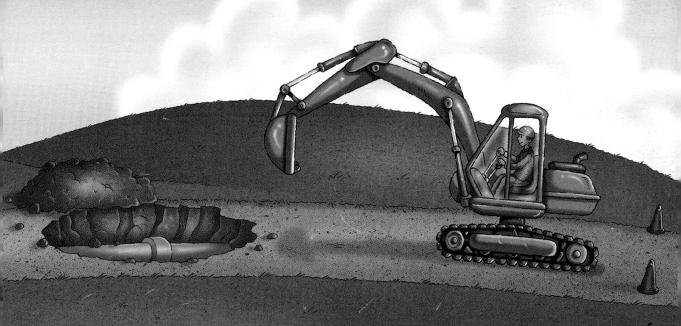

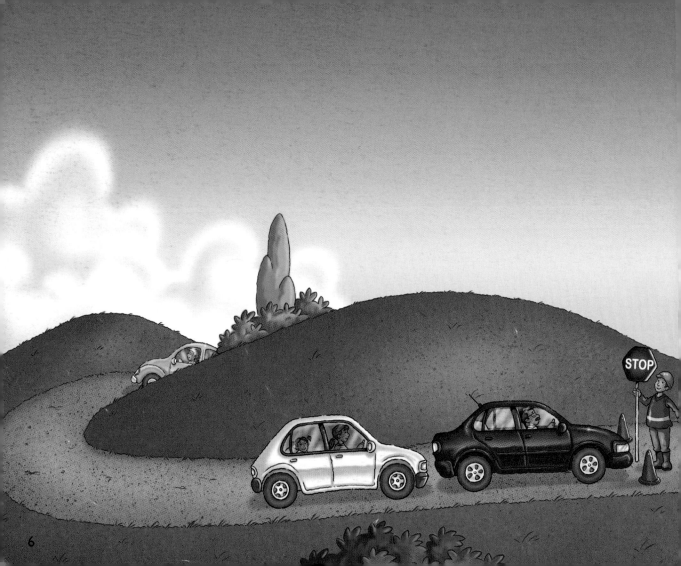

Look at the digger.

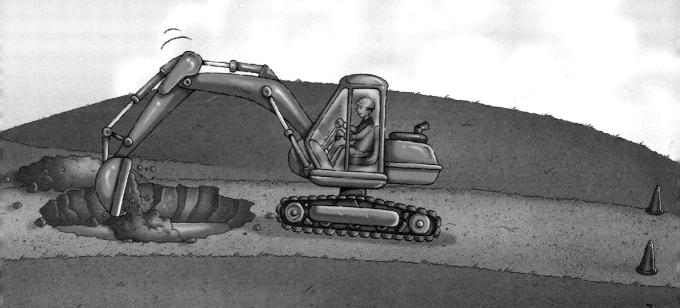

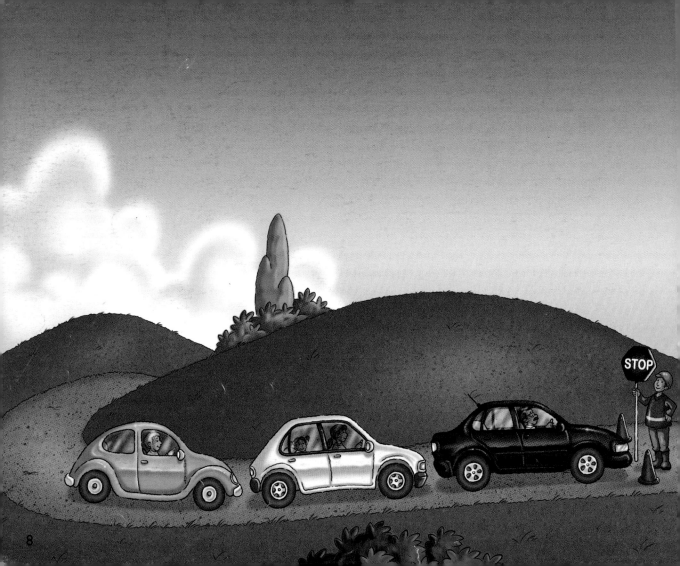

Here is the big truck.

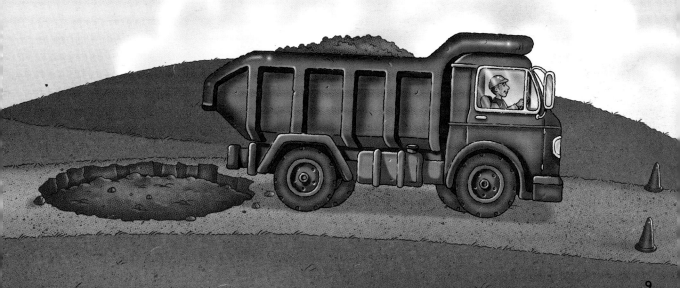

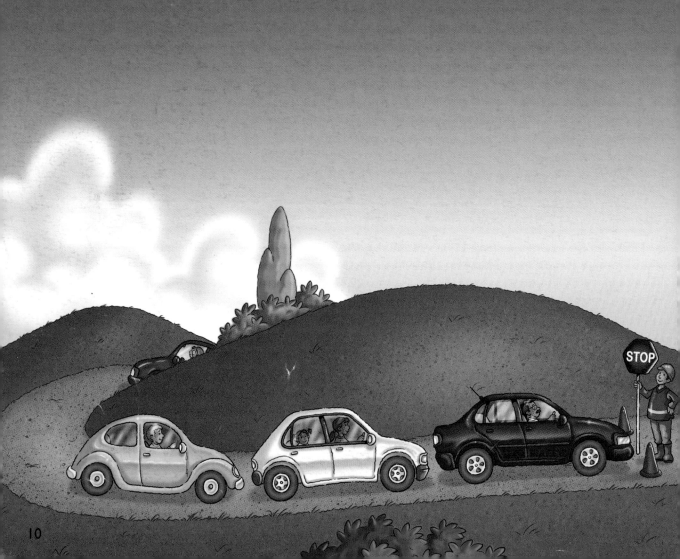

Look at the big truck.

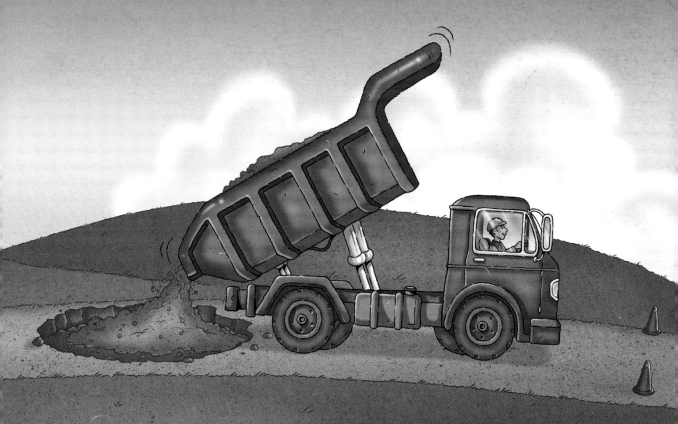

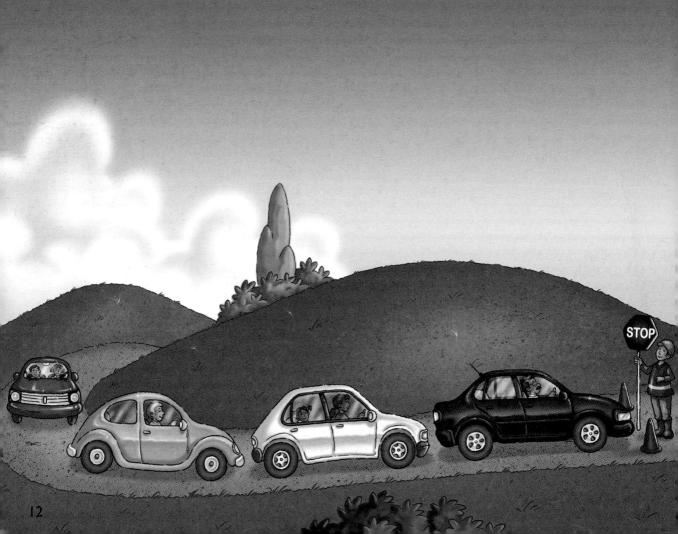

Here is the roller.

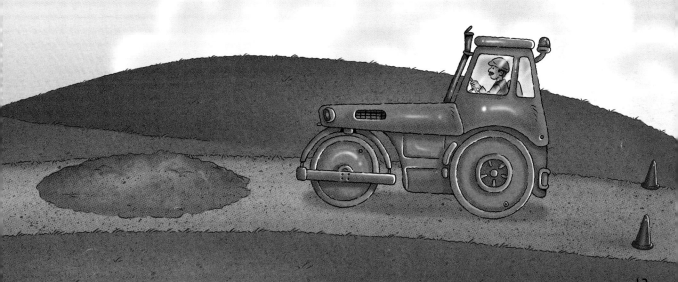

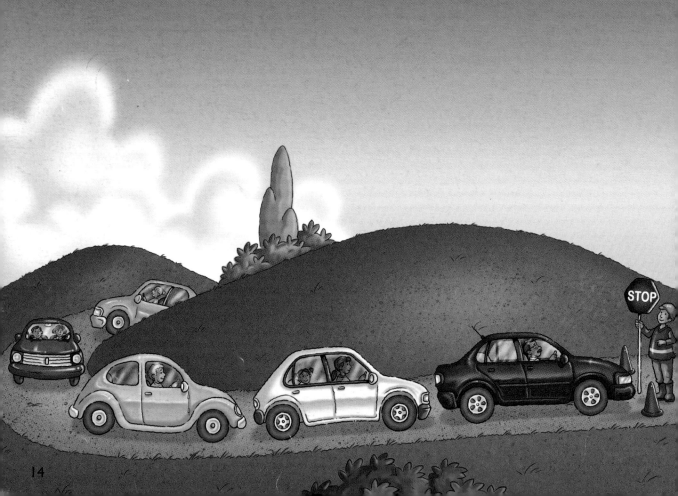

Look at the roller.

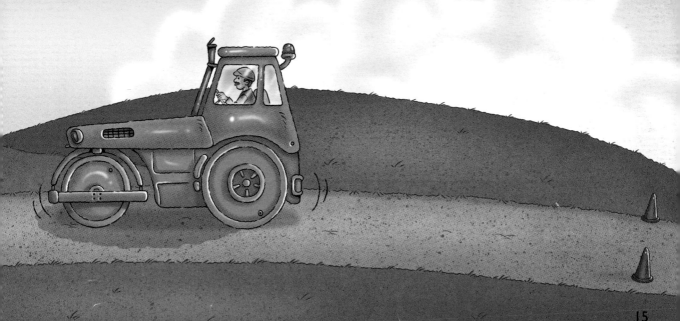

Look at the cars.

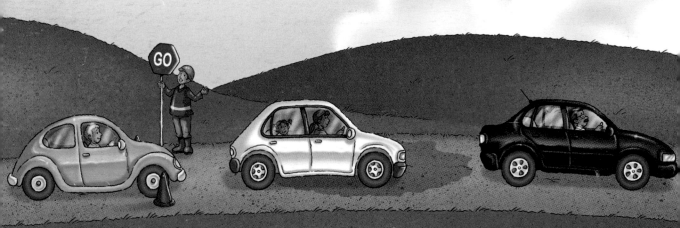